This book belongs to:

Heba

babar

✗ Aliyah

wrote this

GOODWORD

Illustrated by Achla Anand
First published 2004
Reprinted 2014
© Goodword Books 2014

Goodword Books
1, Nizamuddin West Market, New Delhi-110 013
Tel. +9111-4182-7083, Mob. +91-8588822672
email: info@goodwordbooks.com
www.goodwordbooks.com

Goodword Books, Chennai
324, Triplicane High Road, Triplicane, Chennai-600005
Tel. +9144-4352-4599
Mob. +91-9790853944, 9600105558
email: chennaigoodword@gmail.com

Goodword Books, Hyderabad
2-48/182, Plot No. 182, Street No. 22
Telecom Nagar Colony, Gachi Bawli, Hyderabad-500032
Mob. 9448651644
email: hyd.goodword@gmail.com

IB Publisher Inc.
81 Bloomingdale Rd, Hicksville, NY 11801, USA
Tel. 516-933-1000, Fax: 516-933-1200
Toll Free: 1-888-560-3222
email: info@ibpublisher.com, www.ibpublisher.com

Non-Profit Bookstore
Talim-ul-Islam Community Center
86 Rivalda Road, Toronto ON M9M 2M8, Canada
Tel. 416-740-7844
email: lugatulquran@hotmail.com, www.LQToronto.com

Islamic Vision Ltd.
426-434 Coventry Road, Small Heath
Birmingham B10 0UG, U.K.
Tel. 121-773-0137, Fax: 121-766-8577
e-mail: info@ipci-iv.co.uk, www.islamicvision.co.uk

Printed in India

FAVOURITE TALES FROM THE
QURAN

TWO TALES:
The Great Ark
The Beautiful Prayer

Saniyasnain Khan

GOODWORD

The Great Ark

Long long ago Allah sent Nuh عليه السلام with the message of truth. For a very long time, Nuh عليه السلام tried to lead his people to the right path, but only a very few poor people paid any heed. In fact, the rich people tried to harm Nuh عليه السلام. So Nuh عليه السلام prayed to Allah for help and Allah asked him to build an Ark, saying that to punish these bad people, He would send a great flood.

So Nuh عليه السلام, helped by a handful of believers, started building a huge Ark. People laughed at them.

When, after lots and lots of hard and tiring work, the Ark was ready to sail, Nuh عليه السلام asked all the believers to go on board in the name of Allah. Allah told Nuh عليه السلام to bring along a male and a female of every kind of living creature as well.

One by one all the animals entered the
Ark. Some had wings and some had
legs; some crawled and some hopped.
All came right into the Ark in pairs. The
Ark became a huge barn for the animals
and a safe houseboat for the believers.

The animals came running—giraffes and rhinos, elephants and camels, monkeys and wolves, cats and kangaroos, bears and horses, cows and sheep, lions and tigers—and all went into the Ark in pairs. There were chickens and ducks, flamingos and hawks, peacocks and pelicans, ostriches and hens—to name but a few.

9

Birds both tiny and big that flew high above the earth came along too. All were gathered in pairs and led on board. Tortoises, snails and turtles came crawling along the ground.

Then came frogs and grasshoppers who hopped right into the Ark. Rabbits too ran races—let's see who gets on board first! And finally came the crocodiles with their big jaws.

No sooner had all the creatures come on board and the supplies had been stowed away, than black clouds began to cover the sky. First, there was a drizzle, then the rains came. More and more rain fell each day. Day after day, rain and more rain. The whole world seemed to be dark.

It became darker and darker with strong winds blowing from every side and water rising in huge waves as far as the eye could see.

Allah commanded the floodgates of heaven to open and the ground to crack open so that a fountain of water came shooting up. The rivers overflowed and water fell in torrents. The Ark rose and fell on waves as tall as mountains.

More and more water came till the valleys were filled, the trees were covered by the waters and the hills and the mountains sank out of sight. The world was like a huge sea—the only thing one could see was water everywhere.

Far down below, all those who had paid
no attention to the call of the Prophet
Nuh عليه السلام were drowned in the mighty
flood. With the rain hammering on the
roof and a great wind that roared all
around, the Ark went on sailing amidst
the waves.

The thunder rolled and the lightning flashed from the angry skies. Everyone on board was very frightened, but Nuh عليه السلام kept praying to his Lord for His Mercy at this great moment of trial.

When the flood had reached its peak, Allah commanded the earth to swallow up its water and sky to hold back the rain. The water began to dry up. The rain had stopped! The clouds began to part.

As the water began to go down, the mountain peaks began to rear up out of it. The Ark was caught by the peak of Mount Judi, in a land now known as Turkey, and rested upon it. The Prophet Nuh عليه السلام and the believers who were with him thanked Allah for saving them from such a terrible flood. Everyone happily came out of the Ark. The animals were led to safety.

Nuh عليه السلام prayed: "Lord, let my landing from this Ark be blessed, for You alone can make me land in safety.

In this way Allah made the flood and
the Ark of Nuh ﷺ a sign and a warning
for all those who came after the
Prophet Nuh ﷺ.

The Beautiful Prayer

SURAH AL-ANBIYA 21:83-84

The Prophet Ayyub, or Job ﷺ, was a great prophet who lived in the ninth century B.C. He lived in Haran near Damascus in Syria, and set great examples for everyone.

Besides being very wise and kind, Ayyub عليه السلام was also a very rich man. He had huge herds of cattle, vast fields, a large family and many friends.

Yet, he was always a trusty servant of Allah, and kept asking others to worship Him.

But Satan made people think that it was only because Ayyub ﷺ was wealthy that he lived a good life, and that if his blessings were taken away, he would no longer be grateful to Allah.

To put him to the test, Allah caused his cattle, crops, and children to die and, worst of all, Ayyub became very ill, and had to stay in bed for many years.

Very soon, Ayyub عليه السلام became very poor
and his friends left him one by one. But
Ayyub عليه السلام was not angry. He put his
entire trust in Allah, feeling sure that
Allah knew best about everything.

When his suffering and loneliness
became very bad, Ayyub ﷵ turned to
Allah in humble prayer, crying: "I
cannot bear all these ills. But You are
the Most Merciful of all."

Allah heard his beautiful prayer, and put
an end to his long and terrible hardship.
He ordered Ayyub ﷺ to strike the
ground with his feet.

He did as Allah said, and by a miracle, a spring of fresh water gushed forth. No sooner did Ayyub عليه السلام take a bath in it, than his illness was cured and he became strong and healthy again.

Because Ayyub ﷺ had been very patient all this time. Allah not only rewarded him with great gifts in the Hereafter, but made him doubly wealthy in this world. He became so rich that it was said that "he was rained upon with locusts of gold."

He had a new family of seven sons and three daughters. He lived to the ripe old age of 93 and saw four generations.

عَلَيْهِ السَّلَام *Alayhis Salam* 'May peace be upon him.'
The customary blessing on the prophets.